THE
PRESS-OUT AND MAKE
Christmas
GIFT BOX
BOOK

Illustrated by **Sally Hynard** (Garden Studio) *and* **Nicolette Green**

Additional illustration by Pauline Bayne

[DK]

DORLING KINDERSLEY

· London · New York · Stuttgart ·

SNOW BELLS CIRCLES
Page 3

LITTLE ANGEL HEART
Page 5

WINTERGREEN HEART
Page 7

CHRISTMAS STOCKING OBELISK
Page 9

ICE SKATER PYRAMID
Page 11

CHRISTMAS PYRAMIDS
Page 13

ROBIN CASKET
Page 15

SNOW SCENE CASKET
Page 17

A DORLING KINDERSLEY BOOK

Managing art editor
Carole Ash

Editor
Rosie Pearson

Art editor
Sarah Ponder

Production controller
Rosalind Priestley

Paper engineer
Chris Dartnell

First published in Great Britain in 1992 by Dorling Kindersley Limited, 9 Henrietta Street, London WC2E 8PS

Copyright © 1992 Dorling Kindersley Limited, London

Dorling Kindersley would like to thank Martin Cameron, Dave King, and the Dorling Kindersley studio for the photography.

Recipes on page 44 from *Chocolate* © 1989 Jill Norman, published by Dorling Kindersley.

A CIP catalogue for this book is available from the British Library.

ISBN 0-86318-980-6

Typeset by SX Composing Limited, Rayleigh, Essex
Reproduced by Bright Arts (H.K.) Limited, Hong Kong
Printed and bound in Singapore by Imago Productions PTE Limited

FESTIVE GARLAND HEXAGONS
Page 19

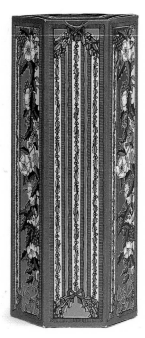

SNOW BELLS
CIRCLES

Assembly
instructions
page 33

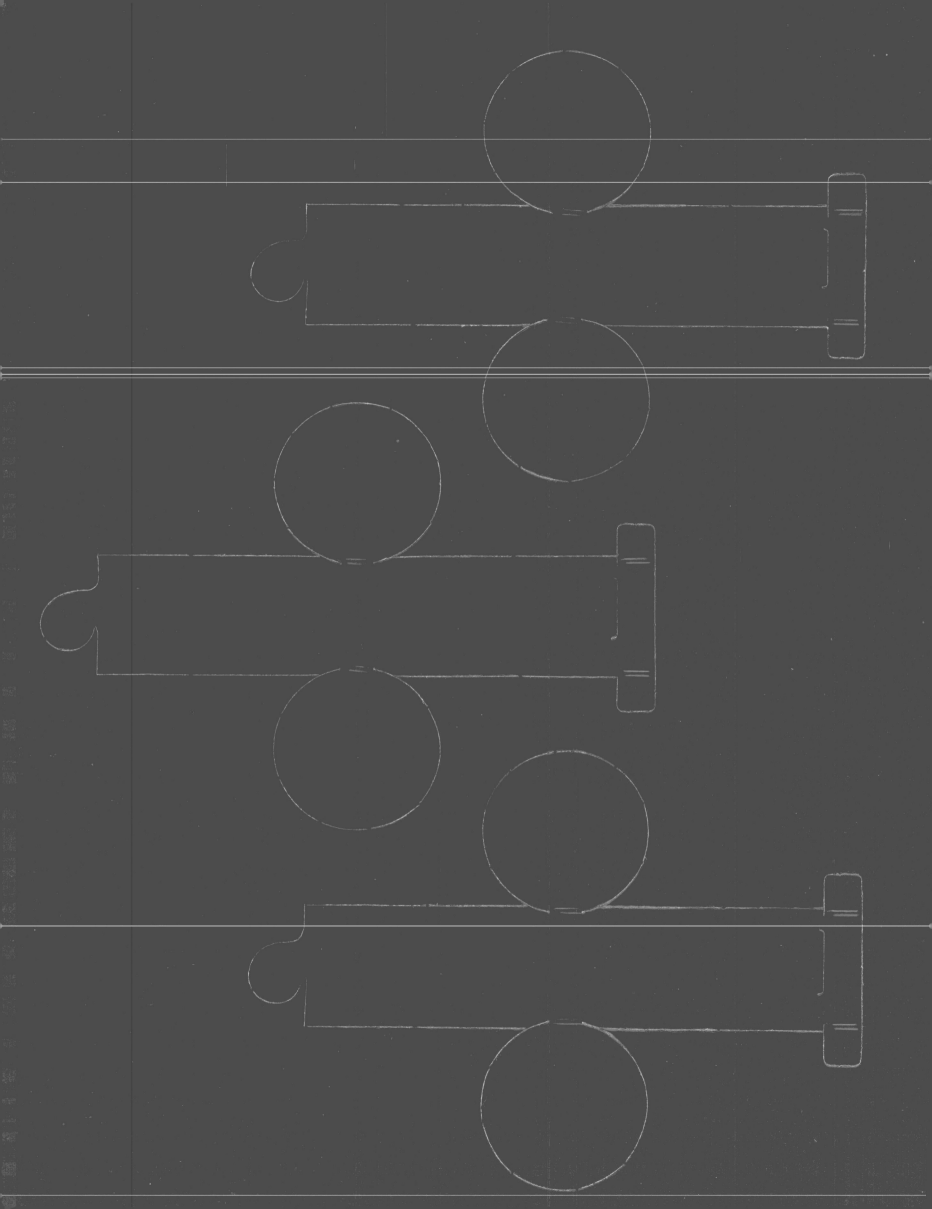

LITTLE ANGEL HEART

Assembly
instructions
page 34

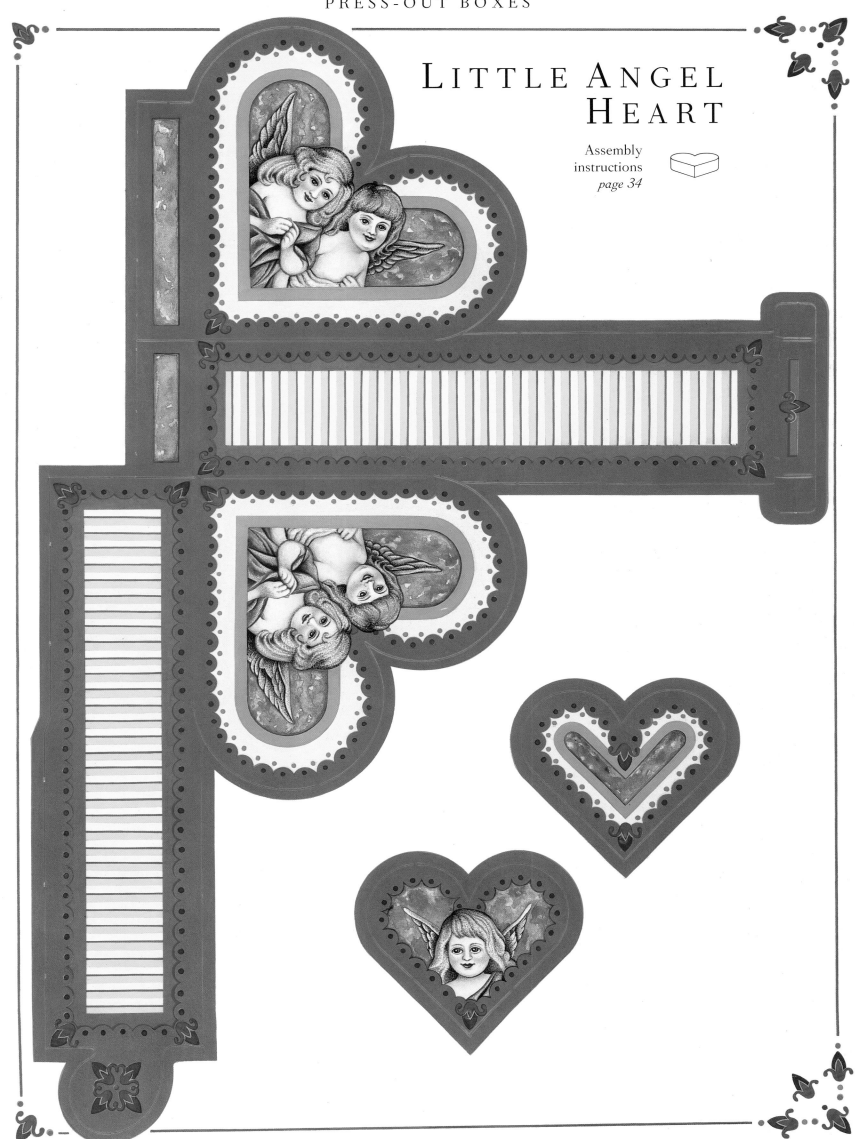

WINTERGREEN HEART

Assembly
instructions
page 34

ICE SKATER PYRAMID

Assembly
instructions
page 36

CHRISTMAS PYRAMIDS

Assembly
instructions
page 36

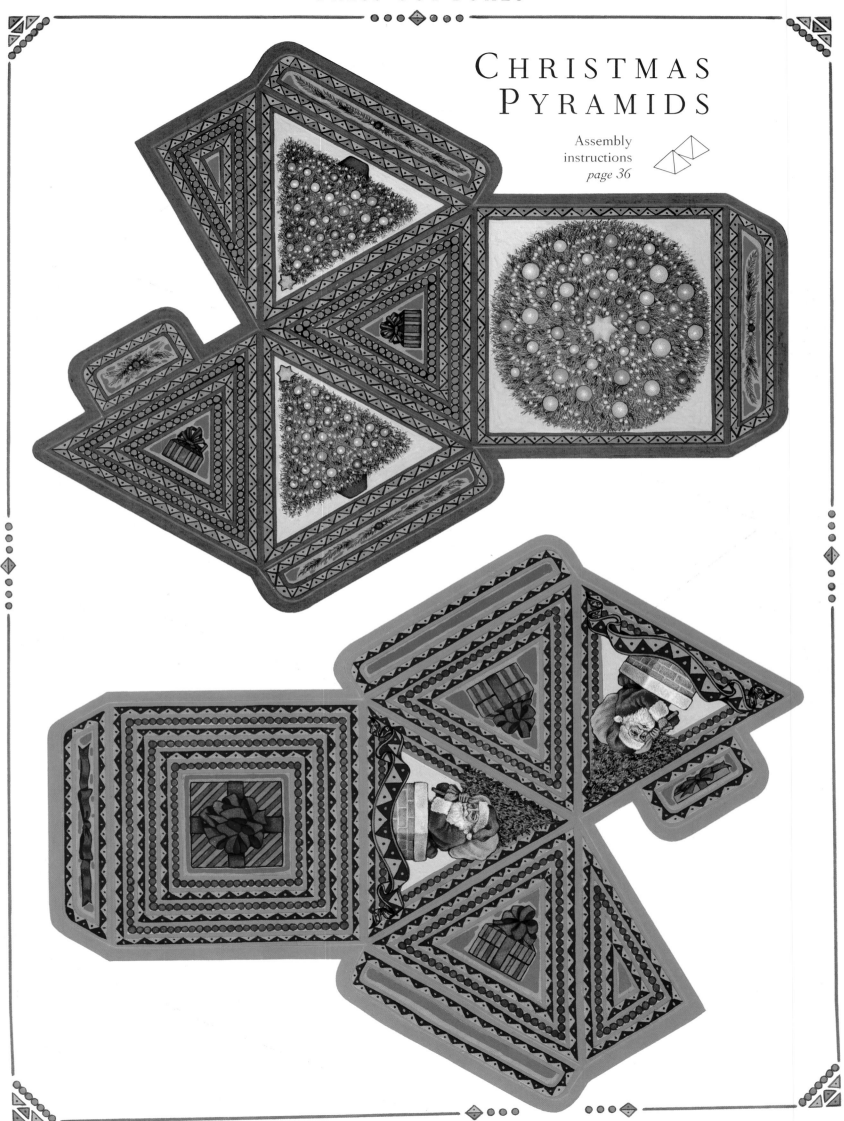

ROBIN CASKET

Assembly instructions
page 37

SNOW SCENE CASKET

Assembly instructions
page 37

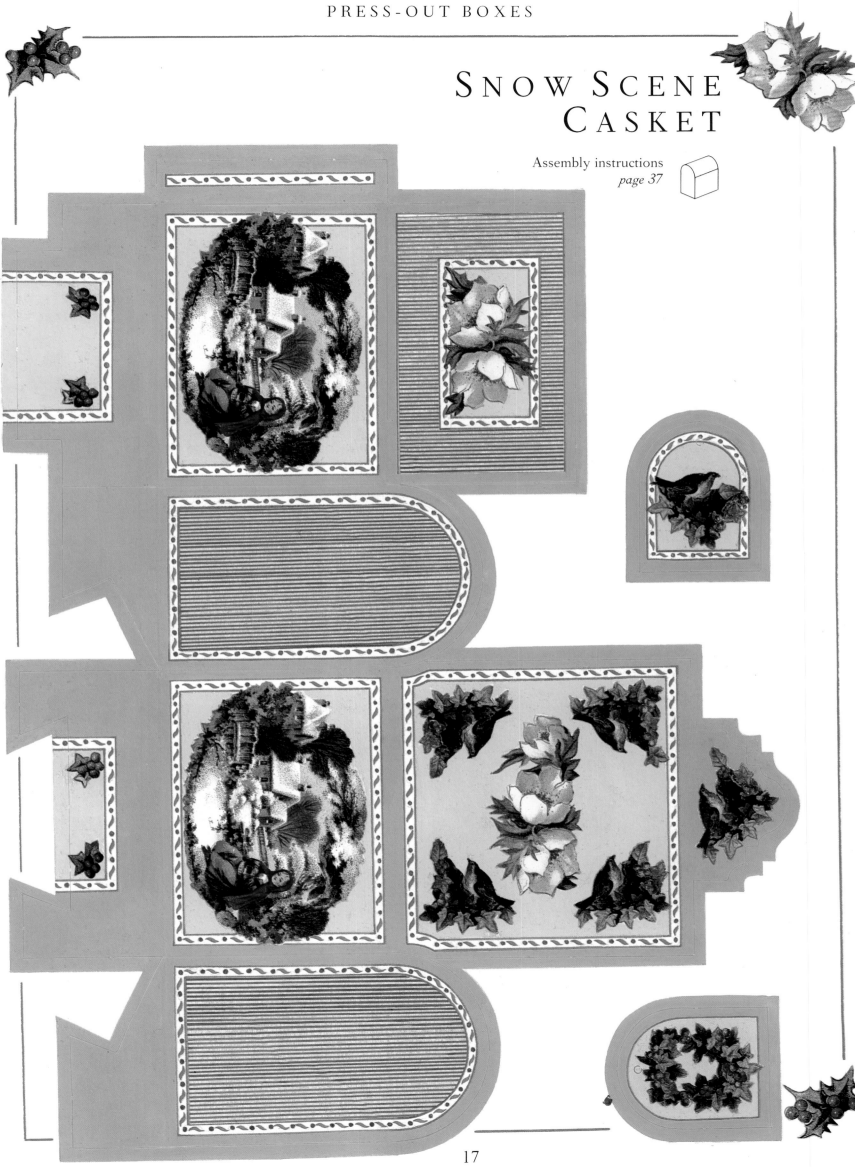

17

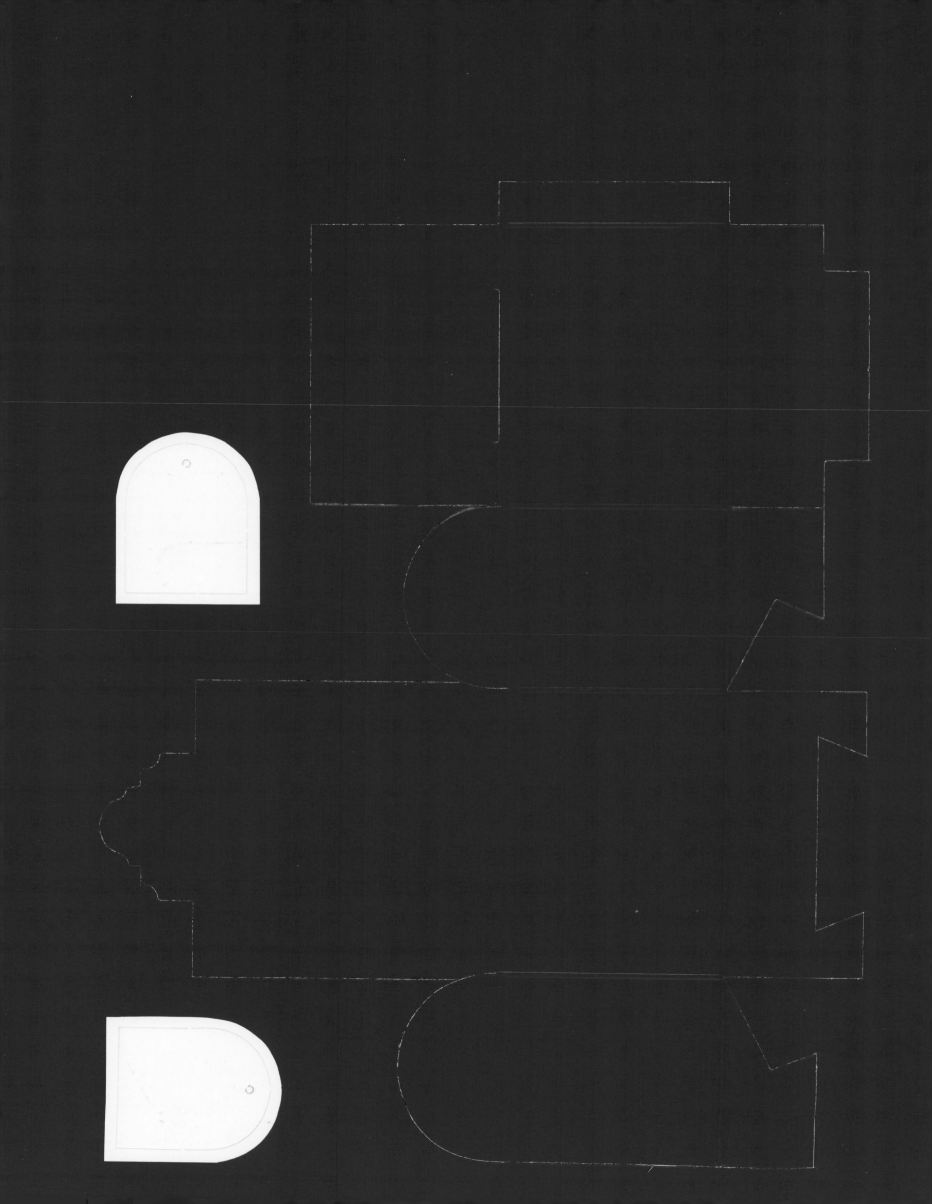

FESTIVE GARLAND HEXAGONS

Assembly instructions
page 41

FROSTED FOLIAGE RECTANGLE

Assembly
instructions
page 38

SANTA CLAUS CUBES

Assembly instructions
page 39

PARTRIDGE & PEAR PRISM

Assembly
instructions
page 40

STARBURST
HALF-PYRAMIDS

Assembly
instructions
page 40

HOLLY BERRY HEXAGON

Assembly
instructions
page 41

WINTER HEXAGONS

Assembly
instructions
page 41

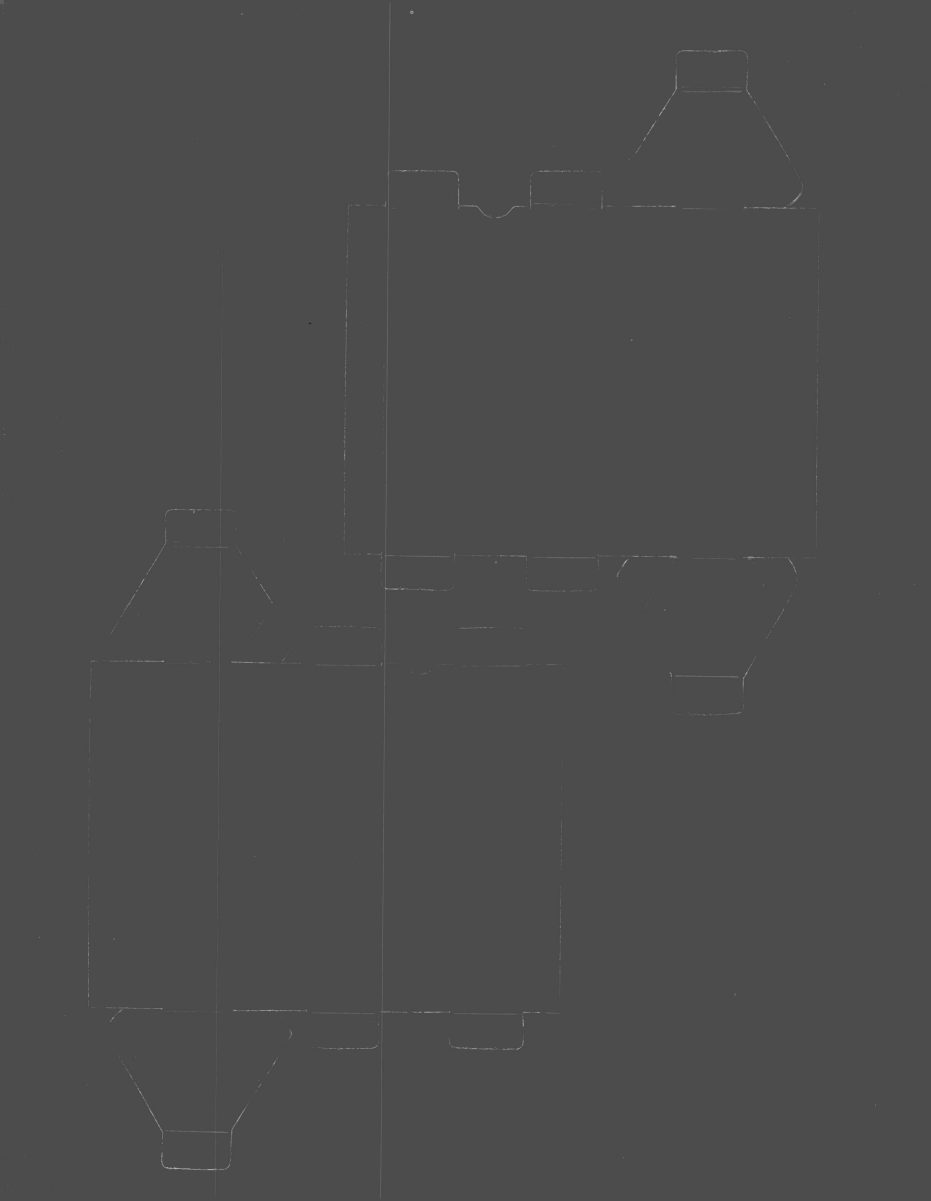

ASSEMBLING THE BOXES

The step-by-step instructions on these pages show how to assemble every box in the book. Instructions are given for each shape of box and apply to all boxes of similar shape, whatever their dimensions. For perfect results, use a quick-drying, clear glue, and spread it thinly on the tabs. You will find it easier to align the sides accurately if you use a glue that does not stick firmly on contact. When you fold along the score lines, sharpen each crease by pressing it with your thumb or the side of a plastic pen. Curved surfaces need to be curled by drawing a ruler or the blunt side of a knife blade along the inside surface of the card.

MAKING A CIRCLE   Press-out boxes on page 3

Circle
Diameter: 43 mm (1⅝ in)
Depth: 33 mm (1¼ in)

1 Press the box out of the page, then place it face down and fold along the score lines.

2 Curl the two rectangular sides by drawing a knife edge or ruler along them (see above) to form the curved walls of the box.

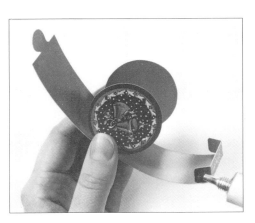

3 Fold the flap in and make sure that the tabs are still bent in, then dab a little glue on the outside of one of the tabs.

4 Stretch the side with the tabs round the rim of the circle so that it fits snugly. Tuck the flap in and press the tab against the side. Dab glue on the other tab, and repeat.

5 Pull the second side round, and close the box by pushing the tongue into the slot on the flap.

MAKING A HEART Press-out boxes on pages 5 and 7

Heart
Top to bottom: 90 mm (3½ in)
Depth: 38 mm (1½ in)

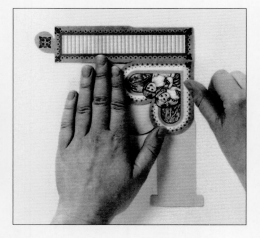

1 Press the box out of the page, then turn it over and fold along the score lines, starting with the long ones beside the heart-shaped sides. Fold the two tiny tabs out rather than in.

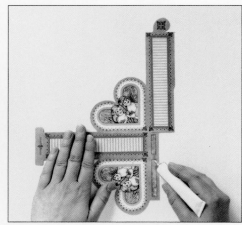

2 Turn the box over and spread glue over the two large tabs.

3 Turn it over again, then fold up both hearts, tucking the shorter glued tab inside the longer one. Align the long tab carefully against the side, and press both tabs until they stick.

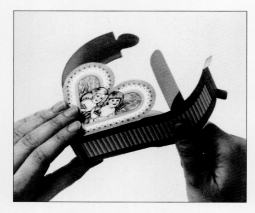

4 Curl both the long rectangular sides against the edge of a knife or ruler (see page 33).

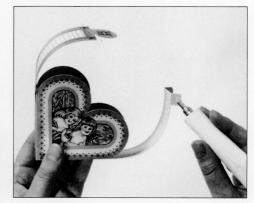

5 Make sure that the two tiny tabs are bent back, then dab a little glue on the outside of each one.

6 Stretch the side with the tabs round the rim of the heart shape so that it fits snugly at the top and bottom edges.

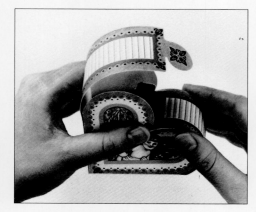

7 Press the tabs against the inside of the heart and hold them in place until they stick firmly.

8 Stretch the second side round the rim of the heart, ensuring that it fits snugly at the edges. Close the box by pushing the tongue through the slot.

MAKING AN OBELISK Press-out box on page 9

Obelisk
Height: 156 mm (6⅛ in)
Base: 52 mm (3⅟₁₆ in) square

1 Press the box out of the page, then turn it over and fold along the score lines, starting with the long ones. Fold the top section accurately.

2 Turn the box over and spread glue sparingly over the long tab at the side of the box.

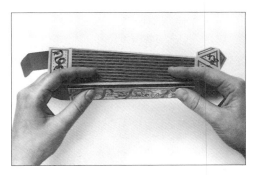

3 Turn it over again and fold the sides round to form the body of the box. Press the glued tab against the side, aligning the edges carefully.

4 Make sure that the sides of the box form exact right angles, then fold up the pyramid section at the top and tuck in the flaps, so that you can see the shape before gluing it.

5 Unfold the pyramid and dab a little glue on all four tabs. Fold the pyramid again, making sure that the edges are accurately aligned.

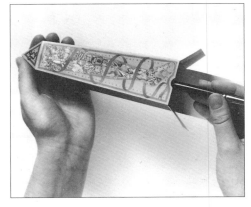

6 Press the tabs from inside with the handle of a narrow brush or a long pencil, to ensure that they stick properly.

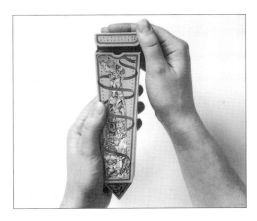

7 Fold down the two flaps at the base, then close the box by tucking the flap into the slot.

MAKING A PYRAMID   Press-out boxes on pages 11 and 13

Large pyramid
Base: 96 mm (3¾ in) square

Small pyramid
Base: 66 mm (2⅝ in) square

1 Press the box out of the page, place it face down and fold along the score lines, starting with the ones radiating from the points of the triangles.

2 Turn the box over and spread glue sparingly on the long tab at the side of one of the triangles.

3 Turn the box over again and, with the square base on the table, fold up two sides to make a pyramid.

4 Press the glued tab on to the base, aligning the edges carefully.

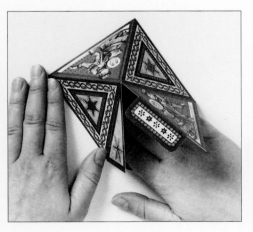

5 Spread glue on the other long tab, then fold the third triangle over and press the tab firmly against the base to form the other side of the box.

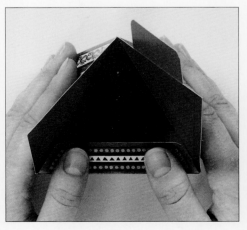

6 Fold up the flap at the bottom edge of the opening.

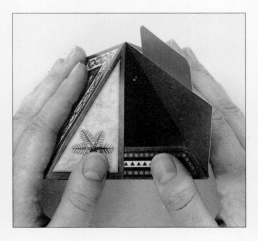

7 Fold the side flap over to cover half the opening.

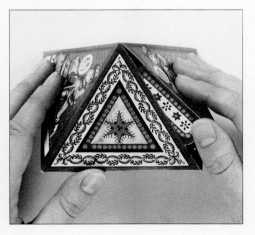

8 Close the box by tucking the tab on the open side into the corresponding slot at the corner.

MAKING A CASKET

Press-out boxes on pages 15 and 17

Casket
Base: 77×50 mm (3×2 in)
Height: 87 mm (3⅜ in)

1 Press the box out of the page, then place it face down and fold along the score lines, starting with the side edges.

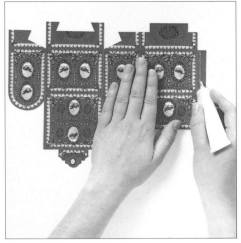

2 Turn it over and spread glue along the tab at the side edge.

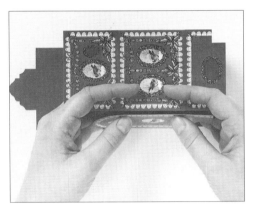

3 Fold the sides of the box round and press the tab against the side, aligning the edges carefully. Hold it until it has stuck firmly.

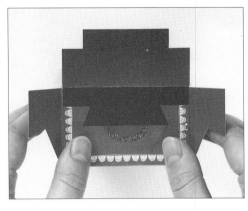

4 Hold the box upside down and fold in the large notched flap.

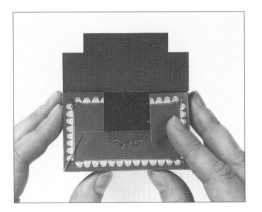

5 Bring over one of the side flaps and push the triangular point under the notch in the first flap. Repeat with the flap on the other side.

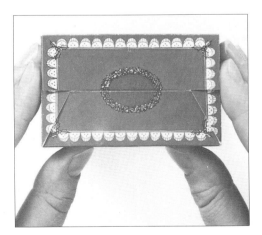

6 Fold down the remaining flap and tuck the tongue into the notch on the first flap. Turn the box over and press the base gently from the inside to make it level.

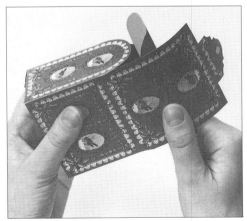

7 Curl the outer lid over carefully by drawing it against the side of a knife or ruler (see page 33).

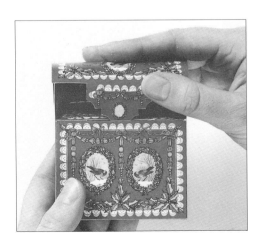

8 Fold in the inner lid, then bring the curved lid over. Slot the flap in to close the lid. If it keeps springing out, put an elastic band round the box until the lid holds its shape.

MAKING A RECTANGLE Press-out box on page 21

Rectangle
Base: 121×60 mm (4¾×2⅜ in)
Height: 40 mm (1½ in)

1 Press the box out of the page, place it face down and fold along the score lines, starting with the longest ones.

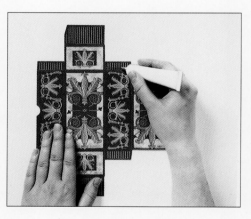

2 Turn the box over and spread glue sparingly over one of the tabs next to the long section that forms the back and lid of the box.

3 Turn the box over again and fold up the section with the glued tab. Align the corner carefully, then press the tab until it has stuck firmly. Repeat with the other tab at the back.

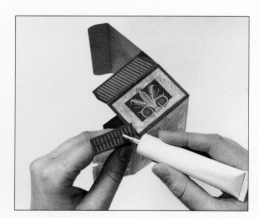

4 Spread a little glue over one of the tabs at the front of the box.

5 Fold up the front section and align the corner carefully. Press the tab until it has stuck firmly, then repeat with the remaining tab.

6 Fold down the two flaps at the sides of the opening.

7 Close the lid by tucking in the flap at the front.

MAKING A CUBE Press-out boxes on page 23

Cube
All sides: 44 mm (1¾ in)

1 Press the box out of the page, then turn it over and fold along the score lines, starting with the ones that form the side edges.

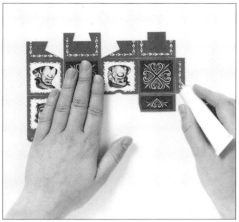

2 Turn it over and spread glue sparingly on the tab.

3 Fold up the four sides of the box and, making sure that the edges are exactly aligned, stick the tab to the side and hold it in place until it has stuck firmly.

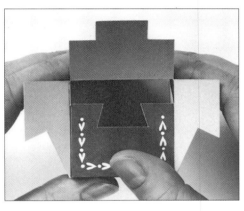

4 Hold the box upside down and fold in the large notched flap.

5 Bring over one of the side flaps and push the triangular point under the notch in the first flap. Repeat with the flap on the other side.

6 Fold down the remaining flap and tuck the tab into the notch on the first flap. Turn the box over and press the flaps from the inside to make sure they form a level base to the box.

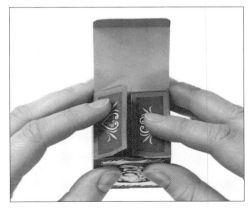

7 Push down the two flaps at the top to cover the opening.

8 Bring the lid over and slot in the front flap to close it.

MAKING A PRISM   Press-out box on page 25

Prism
Length: 150 mm (5⅞ in)
Height: 58 mm (2½ in)

1 Press the box out of the page, then turn it over and fold along the score lines, starting with the long ones.

2 Turn it over and spread glue sparingly along the tab.

3 Turn the box over again and fold it into a triangle. Align the edges carefully, then press the glued tab against the side, holding it in position until it has stuck firmly.

4 Fold in the small flap at the base, then slot in the main one. Close the lid in the same way.

MAKING A HALF-PYRAMID   Press-out boxes on page 27

Half-pyramid
Base: 150 mm (5⅞ in)
Top: 49 mm (1⅞ in)

1 Push the box out of the page, then place it face down and fold along the score lines, starting with the long ones around the square base.

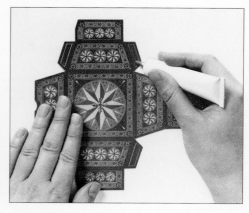

2 Turn the box over and spread glue over one of the tabs by the long section that forms the back and lid. Turn the box over again.

Making a half-pyramid *continued*

3 Fold up the back and the side with the glued tab. Align the corner, then stick the tab to the back. Repeat with the other tab at the back.

4 Fold the two flaps over the opening at the top of the box, then bring the lid down, tucking it behind the tabs at the front. Leave the front itself open.

5 Spread a little glue on the tabs, then fold up the front. Press the front against the glued tabs and hold it until it has stuck firmly.

MAKING A HEXAGON   Press-out boxes on pages 19, 29 and 31

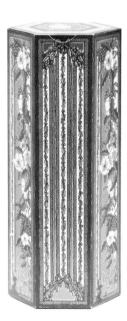

Large hexagon
Height: 155 mm
(6⅛ in)
Diameter: 61 mm
(2⅜ in)

Flat hexagons
Height: 34 mm
(1⅝ in)
Diameter: 63 mm
(2½ in)

Small hexagons
Height: 95 mm
(3¾ in)
Diameter: 38 mm
(1½ in)

1 Push the box out of the page, then turn it over and fold along the score lines, starting with the longest ones.

2 Spread glue sparingly over the tab at the side.

3 Fold the box into a hexagon, align the edges accurately, and press the tab against the side.

4 Support the box in your hand and fold in the flaps at the base.

5 Slot in the third flap to complete the base, then close the lid by folding the flaps in the same way.

FRAGRANT GIFTS

Everybody enjoys receiving luxuriously scented gifts; indeed perfumes and aromatic oils have been traditional offerings throughout the ages. The sweet scent of pot pourri pervading a room, the refreshing tang of lavender impregnating clothes and linen, or the luxury of perfumed toiletries – whatever fragrance you choose, it can be displayed beautifully in a decorative box.

POT POURRI

Whether you opt for a traditional mixture of roses and cottage flowers or prefer an exotic blend of spicy fragrances, you can find pot pourri to suit any taste. If you buy a ready-made mixture, give it a decorative touch of your own: a few miniature dried rose buds add a dainty flourish to a floral pot pourri, and star anise will enhance a spicy blend.

DRIED FLOWERS

A tiny posy of dried flowers scented with essential oils will perfume the room where they are displayed.

SCENTED CANDLES

Combining the gentle warmth of candlelight with a subtle fragrance, scented candles imbue any occasion with a feeling of romantic charm. Try to find candles whose colour and decoration complement their scent.

LAVENDER BAGS AND SACHETS

Perhaps the most popular of all herbal fragrances, lavender is perfect for scenting a wardrobe or linen cupboard. Make small bags in cotton or silk, fill them with dried lavender and tie the neck closed with a ribbon. Alternatively, sew two small pieces of cotton or silk together to make a sachet, trim with lace and fill with dried lavender.

SOAP

Strongly perfumed and attractively shaped, small guest soaps make a delightful gift. If you present them on a bed of pot pourri, the scent of the pot pourri will impregnate the soaps to give them a heady fragrance.

FRAGRANT TOILETRIES

Treat someone to the luxury of a perfumed bath. Bath crystals or salts will scent the bathroom as well as the bathwater, if stored in an open container. Bath pearls dissolve to give a creamy texture to the water.

LAVENDER BATH BAGS

For an unusual gift, make tiny bags in soft cotton, muslin or fine lace and attach a loop of ribbon at the top. Fill them with a mixture of lavender heads, dried flowers, rolled oats and a little grated lemon rind. Suspended by the loop of ribbon under a running tap, the flowers and lemon scent the water, and the oats soften it.

ESSENTIAL OILS

Perhaps the most luxurious of all perfumes, essential oils have been used for centuries for their health-giving properties as well as for their powerful scent. A selection of three or four oils makes a perfect present. They can be blended with vegetable oils to make a massage oil, or a few drops may be added to bathwater.

PERFUME

From the fresh scent of eau-de-Cologne and sweet-smelling floral water, to the pungent fragrance of concentrated perfume, a tiny phial of scent is the ultimate indulgence. An ornate bottle adds to the luxury.

DRAWER FRESHENERS

Sandalwood drawer fresheners give off a spicy fragrance which will impregnate the clothes or linen they are stored with. Drawer fresheners made from other woods may be scented with aromatic oils.

EDIBLE TREATS

At Easter, Christmas, Valentine's Day or on any special occasion, a selection of delicious chocolates, tempting petits fours or mouthwatering fudge is an irresistible treat. Make your gift a visual delight by adding exquisite garnishes and decorations.

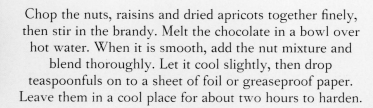

CHOCOLATES

Indulge a chocolate-lover with a box of hand-made chocolates. Introduce variety into your assortment by coating some in vermicelli or chopped nuts, or dusting them with cocoa powder or caster sugar. Pack them in individual paper cases or wrap them in decorative silver paper. The recipes here make about 30 chocolates.

BRANDY AND RAISIN NUGGETS

50g (2oz) blanched almonds   *50g (2oz) dried apricots*
50g (2oz) skinned hazelnuts   *4 tbsp brandy*
75g (3oz) raisins   *140g (5oz) chocolate*

Chop the nuts, raisins and dried apricots together finely, then stir in the brandy. Melt the chocolate in a bowl over hot water. When it is smooth, add the nut mixture and blend thoroughly. Let it cool slightly, then drop teaspoonfuls on to a sheet of foil or greaseproof paper. Leave them in a cool place for about two hours to harden.

RUM TRUFFLES

225g (8oz) plain chocolate   *2 tbsp caster sugar*
50ml (2fl oz) double cream   *2 egg yolks*
75g (3oz) softened butter   *2 tbsp rum*
50g (2oz) cocoa

Melt the chocolate with a tablespoon of water, in a bowl over hot water. Stir in the cream, butter and sugar, a little at a time. Let the mixture cool slightly, then add the egg yolks and rum, and beat until smooth and shiny. Leave it to cool for several hours. Roll portions into small balls and dip each one in cocoa to coat it. Store the truffles in the refrigerator: they will keep for two to three days.

DIPPED FRUIT AND NUTS

Cherries, candied orange peel and Brazil nuts are the most popular centres for dipping in chocolate, but you can coat almost any nut or small fruit – grapes, strawberries, almonds and dried apricots work well, too.

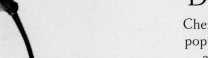

BISCUITS

A box of home-baked biscuits makes a delicious treat.
When you pack them, put greaseproof paper at the bottom
of the box and between each layer of biscuits. The recipes
here make about 40 to 50 small biscuits.

ALMOND PETITS FOURS

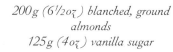

200g (6¹/₂oz) blanched, ground   2 egg whites
almonds   ¹/₂ tsp almond liqueur
125g (4oz) vanilla sugar   glacé cherries for decoration

Mix the almonds and sugar together, then beat the egg
whites until they are frothy and beat this, a little at a time,
into the almond mixture. Add sufficient to form a paste that
holds its shape, but is soft enough to pipe. Mix in the
almond liqueur. Preheat the oven to 350°F/175°C/gas mark 4.
Using a piping bag with a wide tube, pipe shapes about
2.5 cm (1 in) long on to a baking tray lined with
greaseproof paper. Decorate with cherries, then bake until
golden – about 10 to 12 minutes. To remove them from the
tray, pour a little water between the paper and the base of
the tray – the steam will loosen the petits fours.

SPICED BISCUITS

125g (4oz) unsalted butter   ¹/₂ tsp ground cloves
75g (3oz) brown sugar   ¹/₄ tsp ground cinnamon
150g (5oz) flour   ¹/₂ tsp baking powder
¹/₂ tsp ground ginger   sliced almonds for decoration

Cream the butter and sugar, then sift in the flour, spices and
baking powder a little at a time, stirring thoroughly. If the
mixture is very dry, add 1 or 2 tablespoons of water.
Press the dough into a ball, then knead it lightly on a
floured surface until smooth. Roll it into a sausage shape,
wrap in foil and leave to chill for at least two hours.
Preheat the oven to 400°F/200°C/gas mark 6. Cut the dough
into very thin slices, and lay these on a baking tray lined
with greased foil. Decorate each biscuit with sliced almonds,
then bake until golden – about 5 to 7 minutes.

CONFECTIONERY

Bought or home-made fudge, Turkish delight or delicately
flavoured sugared almonds will look delightful displayed in
a decorative gift box. Wrap soft or sticky sweets in coloured
paper or foil.

MARZIPAN FRUIT

Made simply by dyeing marzipan with a tiny amount of
food colouring and shaping by hand, a box of miniature
marzipan fruits makes a delightful present.

SHOPPING SUGGESTIONS

Whatever gift you are searching for, whether something purely decorative or eminently practical, a valuable collectible or some inexpensive trivia, it will take on an air of glamour and luxury when presented in a decorative box. Avoid putting anything very heavy in the boxes, and protect a very small or fragile gift by packing it carefully with some attractive lining (*see page 48*).

JEWELLERY

Small but intricately decorated jewellery complements these boxes perfectly. Strings of beads, rings, brooches and earrings are obvious choices, but cuff-links, silver charms or an antique fob watch are other options. Antique markets are exciting places to hunt for an unusual piece of jewellery.

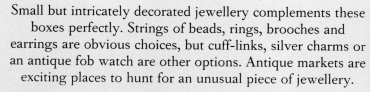

SHELLS

Some of nature's most beautiful creations, shells make an inexpensive, but imaginative and attractive, present. Choose a colour scheme from a range of delicate pinks and lustrous mauves. A sea-horse, a piece of coral or a tiny star fish adds an exotic touch to the display.

BUTTONS

From delicate floral designs to glittering metallic, a set of well-chosen buttons can transform a garment and enhance a chosen style. There are many valuable and collectible buttons on the market, some ornate enough to be worn as brooches. Give a matching set of unusual buttons, or contribute to a collection by finding something unique.

BEADS

Use your imagination when shopping for beads – combine large chunky shapes with more delicate ones, choose an ethnic style or go for sophisticated elegance. Colours and textures can complement the style. Complete the package with some earring findings, or thread and a clasp for a necklace.

STATIONERY

An antique letter opener, an elegant fountain pen or a collection of unusual pencils make ideal presents. Try to find something decorative, to make a change from the usual utilitarian stationery.

BEAUTY PRODUCTS

As an alternative to the ubiquitous collections of make-up and toiletries, look for an unusual handbag mirror, a set of luxurious make-up brushes or a small natural sponge.

FASHION ACCESSORIES

A fine silk scarf, a bow tie or a stylish belt can revive any wardrobe, while clips, combs and ribbons for the hair offer an inexpensive way of creating a new look. Whoever you are buying for, whether you opt for sophisticated evening wear or indulge a taste for the frivolous, some small accessory is always a welcome gift.

SEWING ACCESSORIES

The smallest pieces of sewing equipment are often the most collectible. Antique thimbles are a popular theme for collections, but ornate embroidery scissors or a decorative tape measure may be useful as well as attractive. Other ideas are a selection of embroidery silks in sumptuous colours or a piece of antique lace.

COLLECTIBLES

Anything small and decorative makes a lovely gift. Look out for ornate silver spoons, a pair of tiny candlesticks or something unusual such as an antique coin holder.

LINING THE BOXES

Add the final touch to your package by including some imaginative lining, to protect your gift and add to the impact when the box is opened. Choose the colour and style of your packing material to complement those of the box and the present.

SILK SCARF

A softly folded silk scarf is the perfect background to a small piece of jewellery or a hair accessory, and adds an extra element to the gift.

CRUMPLED TISSUE

Keep a fragile gift safe by making a nest of crumpled tissue paper. Use a double sheet roughly six times the size of your box, curl the edge underneath and crumple the tissue softly until it fits in the box. Push it down gently in the middle to form a well the right size to take your gift.

RIBBONS

Lengths of coiled ribbon can be piled into the box to give a silky-soft lining. Arrange them in loops and tuck in any loose ends. Use several ribbons of the same colour but various widths, or try mixing different colours.

SHREDDED PAPER

Cut or tear narrow strips of tissue paper, then crumple them slightly, to form a soft bed for any gift. Try combining paper of different colours, or for a dramatic glittery effect, use metallic paper or ordinary cooking foil instead of tissue.

ROSE PETALS

Make a delightfully fragrant nest for your gift by piling rose petals into the box. Remember that fresh petals will last for only a day or two before they wilt.

WOOD SHAVINGS

From bold corkscrew curls to narrow ripples in pale colours, wood shavings make an attractive and unusual packaging material for your gift.